I am Pawsö

This book, *I Am Pawso*, is a work of fiction. Names, locations, characters, and situations are the product of the writer's imagination or are used fictitiously. Any resemblance to actual events, locales, animals, or persons, living or dead, is coincidental.

This book details the author's personal experiences with and opinions about mental and physical health. The author is not your mental health or healthcare provider.

The author and publisher are providing *I Am Pawso* and its contents on an "as is" basis and make no representations or warranties of any kind with respect to this book or its contents. The author and publisher disclaim all such representations and warranties, including for example warranties of merchantability and healthcare for a particular purpose. In addition, the author and publisher do not represent or warrant that the information accessible via this book is accurate, complete or current.

The content in this book is not intended to diagnose, treat, cure, or prevent any condition or disease. Please consult with your own physician or healthcare specialist regarding the suggestions and recommendations made in this book.

Except as specifically stated in this book, neither the author or publisher, nor any authors, contributors, or other representatives will be liable for damages arising out of or in connection with the use of this book. This is a comprehensive limitation of liability that applies to all damages of any kind, including (without limitation) compensatory; direct, indirect or consequential damages; loss of data, income or profit; loss of or damage to property and claims of third parties.

This book is not intended as a substitute for consultation with a licensed healthcare practitioner, such as your physician or mental health clinician. Before you begin any healthcare program, or change your lifestyle in any way, you will consult your physician or another licensed healthcare practitioner to ensure that you are in good health and that the examples contained in this book will not harm you.

This book provides content related to physical and/or mental health issues.
Use of this book implies your acceptance of this disclaimer.

In the event you are experiencing a crisis, please call 911, go to the nearest Emergency Room/Hospital, and/or call 988, the Suicide & Crisis Lifeline.

To request permissions, contact the publisher at casey@caseyhersch.com

Hardcover: ISBN 979-8-9871745-0-0
Paperback: ISBN 979-8-9871745-1-7
Ebook: ISBN 979-8-9871745-2-4

Library of Congress Number: 2023907235

Cover art, Photographs of Pawso, Mama, Grandma, and Illustrations by Scott Hersch

Published by Casey Hersch in the United States of America

A message from the Author:

Life can be stressful and unpredictable. Children need options to help them feel capable, confident, and in control.

I Am Pawso is a collection of Pawso Practices (coping skills and lessons) that empower children to connect their minds and bodies. In the story, Pawso repeatedly uses a "shake and turn" to symbolize what he can do to feel better, calm down, and turn around difficult situations.

As you read, think about how you can use Pawso's Shake and Turn Tools and come up with some of your own.

Want more lessons, activities, and discussion questions? Download the free **Parent, Teacher, Clinician Companion Guide**.

www.caseyhersch.com/guide

www.CaseyHersch.com

Pawso's Read-Along Activity

When Pawso gets upset or has a bad day, he uses his collection of Pawso Practices. These practices are the things Pawso can notice, think, say, and do, that help him shake away the bad feelings and turn them around into something positive.

As you read the story, some pages have a colored paw print on the bottom right corner. When you see one, turn to the Pawso Practices page. Find the same color paw print. Read the Pawso Practices in that same colored list. Pick the practices that describe what Pawso either notices, thinks, says, or does on that story page to turn around the situation and feel better.

Which Pawso Practices can you use today?

Pawso Practices:

Things I Do

Helping others makes me happy.
I learn from my mistakes.
When I wear something I like, I feel confident.
Listening to music and moving my body makes me feel good.
I have talents and gifts (inner powers) that help me manage stress.
I continue to learn about myself and others.
I use my talents and skills to create something I like.
I go to my special spot when I need to calm down.
When I don't feel safe, I can walk away or make a new rule.
I can let out my anger using my words instead of fighting back.

Things I Say

I use my words to tell others how I feel.
I name the behaviors I do not like.
I say "thank you," when others are nice to me.
I say, "sorry," when I hurt someone's feelings.
It's OK to tell adults how I feel and what I need.
I ask a trusted adult for help.

Things I Think

I try to understand the other side of the story.
I try to understand people who are not like me.
I remember important lessons from special people in my life.
I remember how special and important I am.
When I think positive thoughts, I feel confident.
When I use my imagination, I can be anything I want to be.

Things I Notice

When I accept who I am, I feel better.
I feel scared in new situations.
My body gives me signals that tell me when I am angry.

To my lifetime cat family who gives me unconditional love, companionship, wisdom, compassion, and the strength to go through life.
I am here because of you.

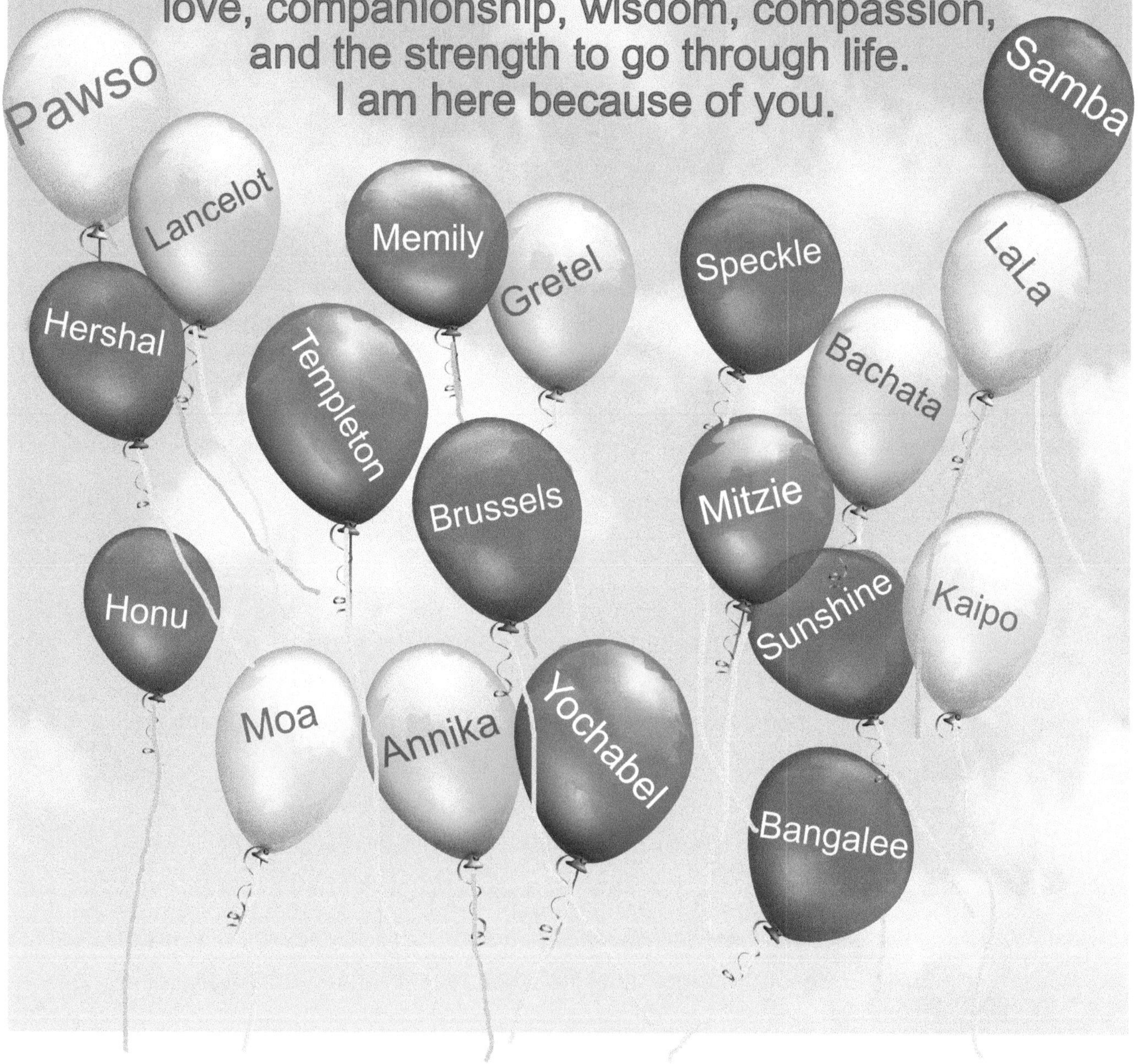

Pawso
Samba
Lancelot
Memily
Gretel
Speckle
LaLa
Hershal
Templeton
Bachata
Brussels
Mitzie
Honu
Sunshine
Kaipo
Moa
Annika
Yochabel
Bangalee

Chef
by Casey Hersch, LCSW
Pictures by Scott Hersch
I am Pawso
Pluto

I am Pawso, a foster cat, and here's my story for you.
Has someone hurt your feelings?
I understand! Me too!

When I get hurt, I feel sad or mad.
One mean word and my mood turns bad.
I used to get upset, shut-down, and hide,
until I learned how to care for
my feelings inside.

I change my thoughts
when my emotions bother me.
I use my mind and body to set me free.

Come along! We can start right now.
Let's use our shake and turn.
I will show you how!

On a bright summer day, I climb a tree
and look from the top to see what might be.
I spot a new friend and wave hello.
She smiles, so I jump down below.

We laugh and sing as we flip round and round
on the jungle gym at the new playground.
"My name is Pawso," and then comes the blow.
"Go! Picasso, you're moving too slow!"

Picasso? Hey! That is not me!

I am Pawso! The one and only!

My fur stands up, my claws ready to strike.

Name calling is a behavior I really don't like.

But for a moment, my mind starts to churn.
I can change my thoughts with a shake and a turn!

Picasso, you say. Picasso, the Great?
The artist with talents and skills to create?
I imagine myself in this special part,
with an easel and paint, I brush fine art.

I end my day very calm and sure,
knowing that I can unruffle my fur.

At summer camp, the days get hotter.
The counselors take us down to the water.
The water scares me, but everyone swims.
Cats crowd my space, and my courage dims.

I am Pawso! I can do this! I want to belong.
I put on my swim gear and pretend to be strong.
Everyone laughs at me. Why are they rude?
I try not to care, but their words change my mood.

I stare at the water hiding my frown.
"Pluto is a Fraidy-Cat! He might drown!"
"Wait! I am Pawso! It's not nice to tease.
Lifeguard! Stop these bullies, PLEASE!"

But for a moment, my mind starts to churn.
I can change my thoughts with a shake and a turn!

Like the dwarf planet Pluto, I am smaller than Earth.
But my value is huge. I know my worth.

Meanies cause hurt feelings to bubble.
I avoid bullies to lessen my trouble.
Today, I am not getting into the pool.
When I don't feel safe, I make a new rule.

I end my day with a calm state of mind,
awaiting the next adventure I find.

This morning, I played outside in the sun.
My stomach hurt, but I still had fun.
Now, my head is dizzy. I must lie down.
Mom says, "Let's see the doctor in town."

Doctor Bengal takes notes and scans my chart.

"Possum," he says, "Let's check your heart."

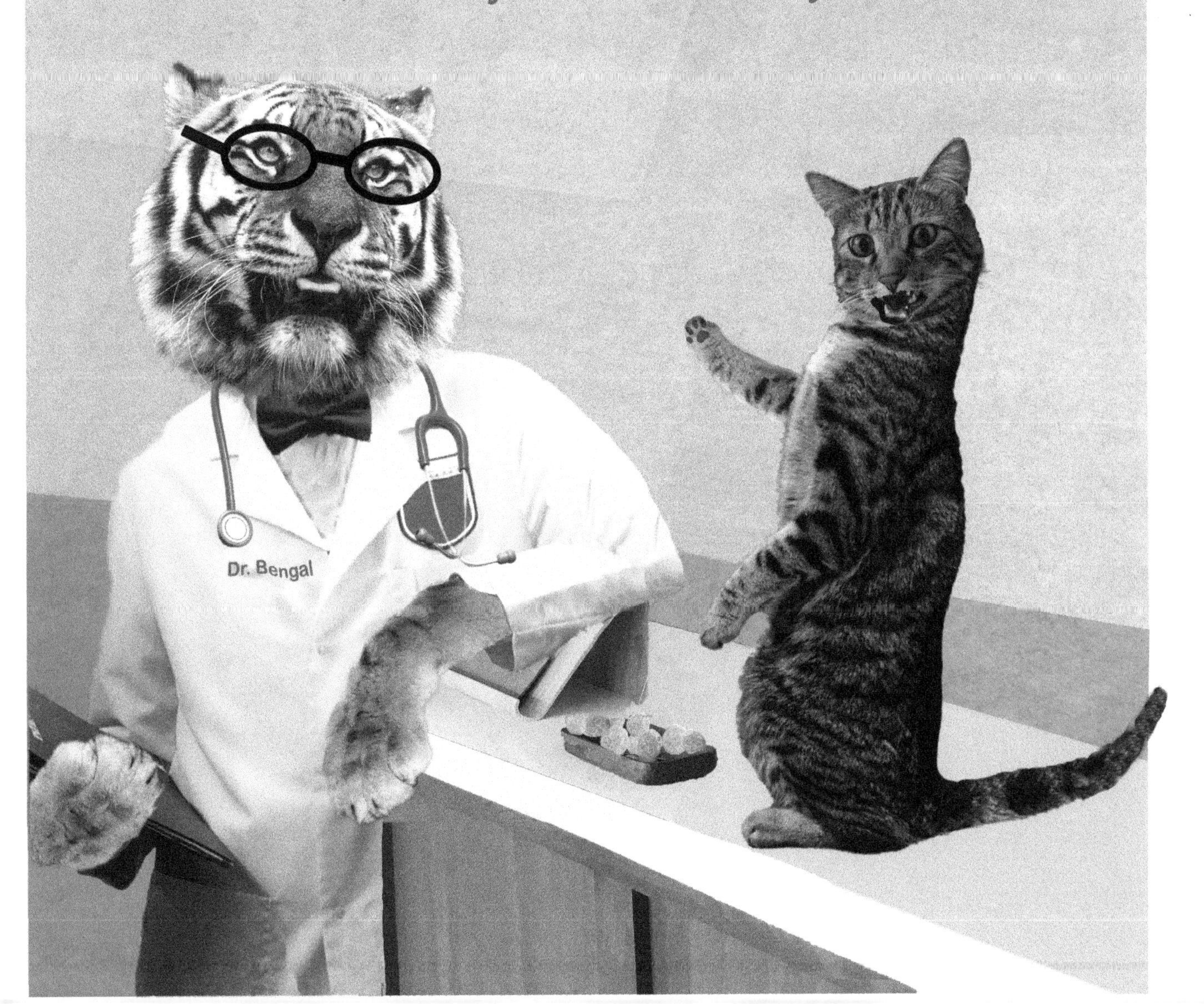

My face feels hot, and my whiskers flitter.
He just called me the wrong darn critter!
The doctor seems nice and doesn't mean harm,
but he hurt my feelings and tripped my alarm.
Picasso
Pluto
I am Pawso!

But for a moment, my mind starts to churn.
I can change my thoughts with a shake and a turn!

Possums, like me, nap in the day.
When nighttime comes, they are ready to play.
I've never seen one asleep on my couch.
I hear they keep babies in a front pouch!

When possums feel scared, they freeze or play dead.

When I feel stressed, I shake n' turn instead.

I don't play dead or trip my alarm!

My teeth look sharp, but I will not harm.

I am trying hard not to seem like a brat.
"Doctor Bengal, like you, I am a cat!
I know adults make mistakes, too,
but calling me Pawso would help me trust you."

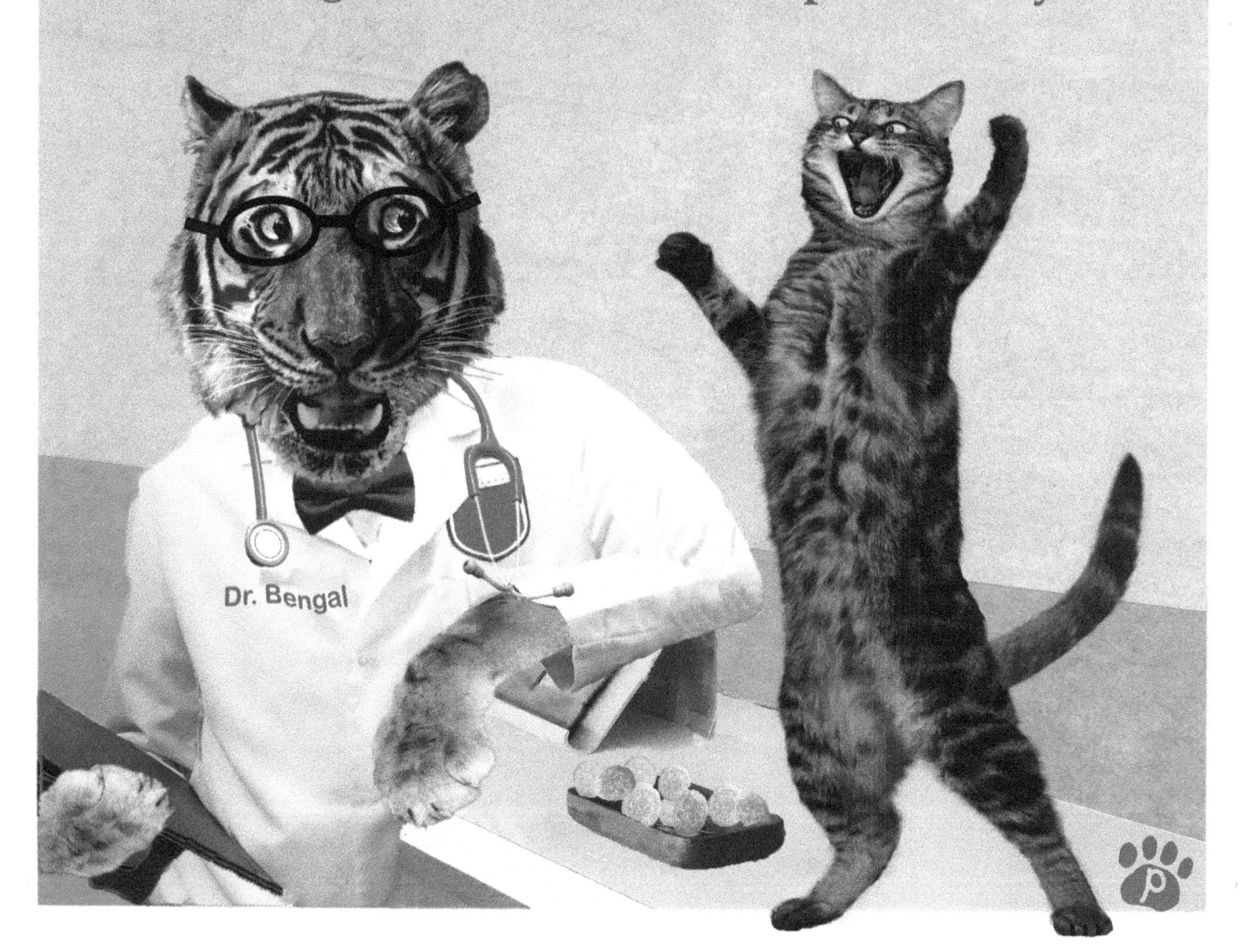

I leave the doctor's confident and sure
that I can speak-up and feel secure.

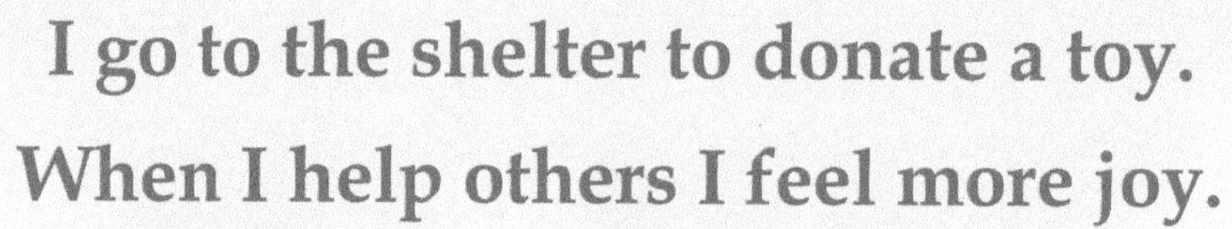
I go to the shelter to donate a toy.
When I help others I feel more joy.

I stop to join a dance in the street.

"Yay! New cultures and friends to meet!"

A cat stomps on my tail and I yell, "Ouch!
My name is Pawso! Don't be a grouch!"

"Sorry," he cries,"I should watch my step.
When I hear music, I am full of pep.
At this fiesta, they call me Head Honcho.
I will show you around, Señor Poncho."

"Head Honcho," I say, "you misunderstood!
Call me Pawso, and we are friends for good!"

Head Honcho

What is wrong with my name? He can't say it right.

I feel angry, though I will not fight.

But for a moment, my mind starts to churn.
I can change my thoughts with a shake and a turn!

I am upset, but names are just words.
No need to fuss because he misheard.
I know Head Honcho doesn't talk like me.
I wonder if he just hears differently.

As the rain falls, Head Honcho holds out his hand.
"Take this poncho to stay dry where you stand."

I throw the wool fabric over my head
and remember the words my grandmother said.
A gift from a friend is a kind gesture.
Say,"Thanks." Don't let bad feelings fester.

"Head Honcho a poncho is the perfect warm gift.
Thank you! I needed this attitude shift."

Pawso blurts out, "I have one addition!
You just started a family tradition!
We can all wear ponchos, just like you.
You are part of my family, and a friend, too."

I end my long day with new thoughts inside.
I accept my name, Pawso, with more pride.

On the first day of school I am a cool cat,
although I feel scared about having to chat.
I sit at my desk, alone and shy,
when a gray fluffy feline catches my eye.

I want to say, "Hi," but I don't know how.
"My name is Pawso, M-E-O-W."
"My name is Peggy," she says in my ears.
"Piggy!" I say, and she bursts into tears.

"Don't call me Piggy! You mean alley cat.
Pawso, take back your words or SCAT!"

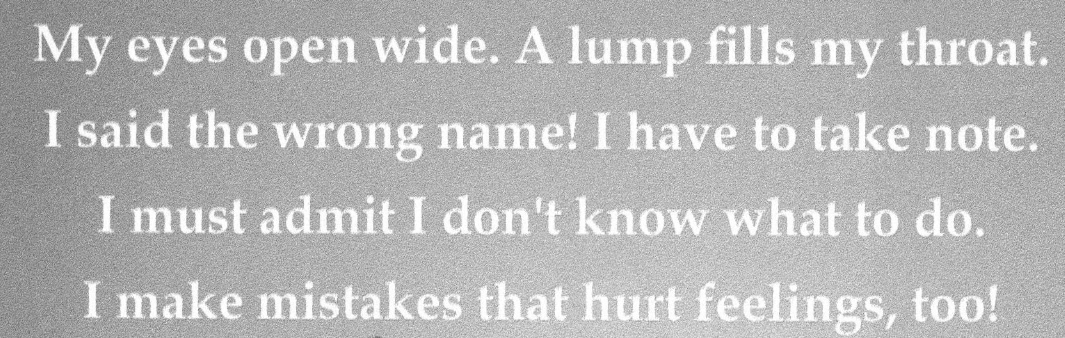

My eyes open wide. A lump fills my throat.
I said the wrong name! I have to take note.
I must admit I don't know what to do.
I make mistakes that hurt feelings, too!

"Peggy, I am sorry. Now I know who you are.
Name calling is mean, and words leave a scar.
I make a choice right here, this hour.
I use my words to always empower."

Our teacher, Ms. Cha-Cha, calls names on the list.

I sit and wonder. Will my name exist?

It happens again, like the times before.

She calls me Pasta. Oh no! Please, no more!

But this time I smile. I know how to learn.
I can change my thoughts with a shake and a turn!

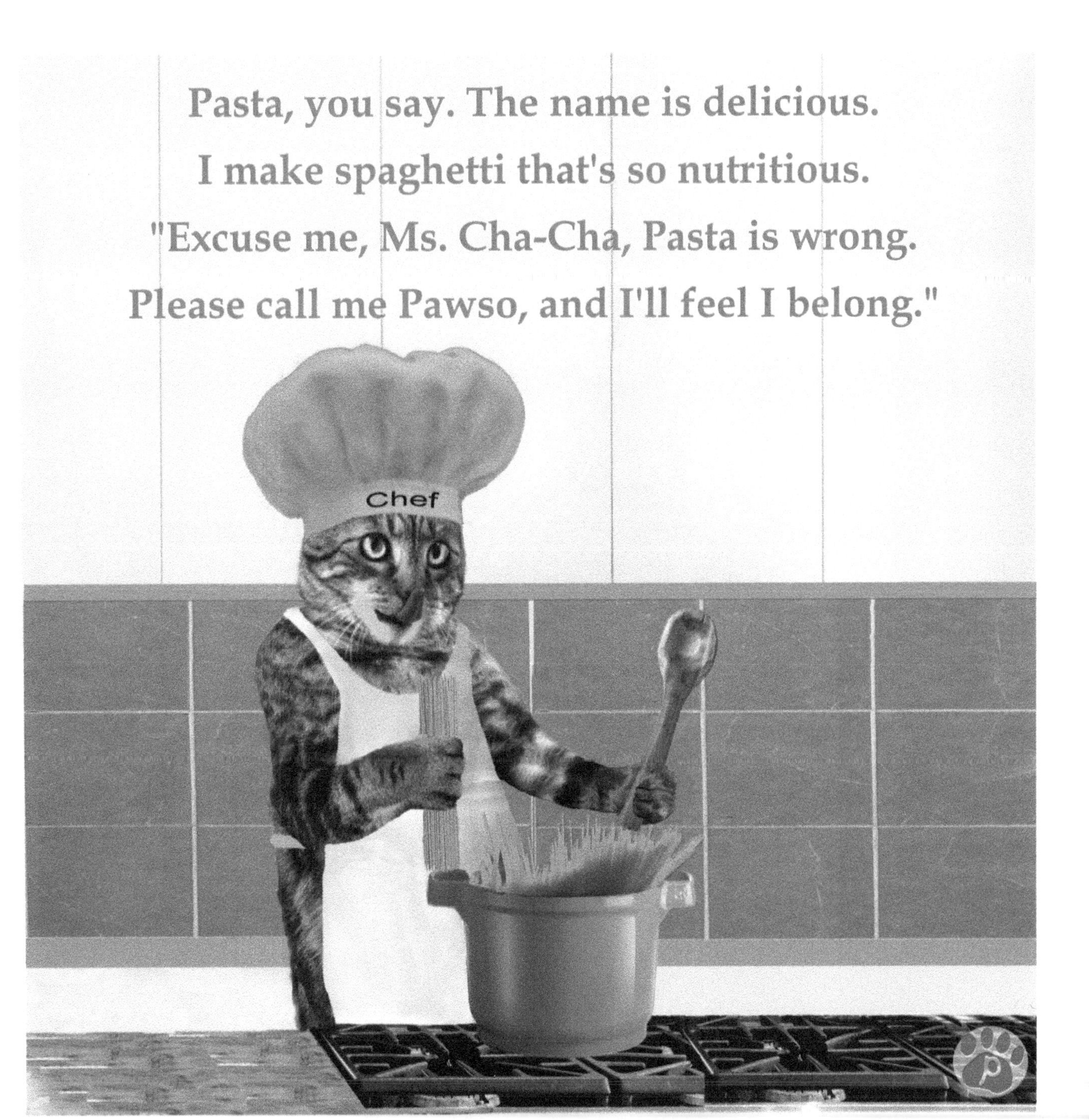
Pasta, you say. The name is delicious.
I make spaghetti that's so nutritious.
"Excuse me, Ms. Cha-Cha, Pasta is wrong.
Please call me Pawso, and I'll feel I belong."
Chef

I look at Peggy. She is still in a frazzle.
At recess I say, "Let's make ourselves dazzle."
"How," she asks, "is there really a way?"
"Sure, let me tell you what I do each day."

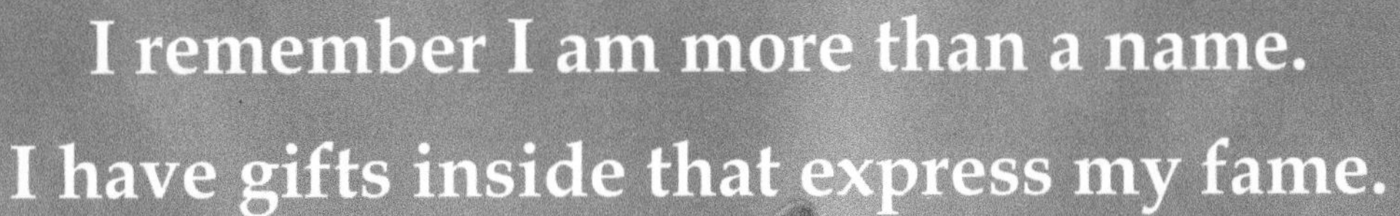
I remember I am more than a name.
I have gifts inside that express my fame.

When I feel angry,
I still have my voice.
I can turn things around
and make the right choice.
My pawsitive choice

My mind can create a positive spin.
I can turn my frown into a grin.
p

Peggy relaxes with grace and style.
She looks at me and flashes a smile.
"Pawso, I don't need to be sour.
You helped me find my inner power!"

We finish the day playing at the park.
Our lessons give us a joyful spark.

Remember that when hurt feelings stir,
there is a way to find your purr.
Move your body and use your mind.
Share your feelings. Take time to unwind.

Expand your view and continue to learn.
You can change your thoughts
with a shake and a turn!

A message from Pawso:

When I was a kitten I felt worried and anxious.
Noises, dogs, and people petting my fur scared me.
I protected myself by biting and hiding.
I felt sad and alone. No one wanted to adopt me.
Fortunately, my foster mom, Casey, brought my sister, Samba, and me home.
Casey is a therapist: A nice person who talks about feelings and helps you work on problems.
Casey gave me tips to calm down and ways to help me feel better!
Now I am a capable and confident cat.
I still work on my problems, but I have skills and people to help me.
I feel pawsitively purrfect being me.

Pawso

www.IAmPawso.com

If you enjoyed *I Am Pawso*, please write a review on Amazon and Goodreads.
Your review is essential to my success and ensures Pawso's story is accessible to all.
Get FREE Pawso Kids Games and Activities:
www.caseyhersch.com/games
Apply Pawso Practices and Shake and Turn Tools in your home, school, or program with a FREE parent, teacher, clinician Guidebook
www.caseyhersch.com/guide

Glossary:

Bengal: A Tiger from India known for its yellow and black stripes.

Empower: Feeling as though you can make choices to improve your life.

Fame: When you are known and recognized for your talents.

Feline: A category that includes all animals (wild or domestic) in the cat family.

Fiesta: A festival, party, or celebration in Spanish speaking countries.

Foster: A temporary situation where a person provides care to an animal or child in a home or safe place.

Head Honcho: A title for a leader or person in charge.

Inner Power: Your talents, gifts, and special abilities that help you live a healthy, happy, and successful life.

Picasso: Pablo Ruiz Picasso (1881-1973). A famous Spanish artist.

Pluto: A dwarf planet in our solar system.

Poncho: A blanket or piece of cloth with a hole in the center for your head often worn to stay dry or keep warm.

Possum: An animal in the marsupial category who raise their babies in a pouch.

Señor: A title in the Spanish language used to politely address a man. Similar to Mr. in English.

Shelter: A temporary place where lost or homeless cats and dogs live until they find a home.

Shut-Down: When you ignore feelings, avoid people and activities, and stop talking.

Tradition: Beliefs, stories, celebrations, holidays, or activities that families share with each other and continue year after year.

Milton Keynes UK
Ingram Content Group UK Ltd.
UKHW050323301123
433429UK00003B/54